MW00437619

Birds

If you should see birds
sitting in a row,

count them up quickly
your fortune to know.

One

you'll be happy.

Two

you'll be sad.

Three

for some good news.

Four

news that's bad.

Five

you'll have silver.

Six

you'll have gold.

Seven for a secret
that's never been told.